BY DAVID & EMBERLI PRIDHAM

ILLUSTRATIONS BY ANYU ROUAUX

If not you, then who?

LET THE GAMES BEGIN!

If Not You, Then Who?

Let the Games Begin!

ISBN 978-1-951317-08-9

Published in the United States by Weeva, Inc.

First Printing, 2020

Story by David and Emberli Pridham with special assistance by Hayley Irvin of Weeva, Inc.
Creative direction by Emberli Pridham
Illustrations by Anyu Rouaux
Graphic design by Rachel Bostick of Weeva, Inc.

Weeva
701 Brazos Street
Austin, TX 78735

www.weeva.com
Hello@Weeva.com

Available at bookstore.weeva.com

To children everywhere—the dreamers of today are the inventors of tomorrow, and the ideas of today are tomorrow's most important inventions. Never forget that you can change the world with your mind!

"If we all did the things we are really capable of doing, we would literally astound ourselves..."

—Thomas Edison

We like to say that the story of invention is the story of America. Nowhere is this more true than with sports. Around the world, America is known for the games we play. Everyone in our family identifies with their favorite sport. We play tennis and golf together all the time and use that time together to build a stronger family. Our children love soccer, basketball, and the occasional game of bocce. All of these games were created by inventors and continue to evolve as inventors make those sports better. We want to use this book as an opportunity to introduce you to some of those games and the inventors that brought them to us.

Emberli & David Pridham

Every Friday, the Fairley family played tennis together. Sometimes they would play teams and sometimes they would play one on one, but they always had fun and never kept score.

Sometimes they played by their own rules, and that was fun, too.

"Brooke, Noah, let's pick up the tennis balls before we leave," Mom said.

Brooke pulled her homemade ball pick-upper out of her tennis bag. "I bet I can pick up more balls than you, Noah!" Brooke shouted as she raced around the court.

But Noah had his own solution that was just as fast!

Tennis is fun, but chasing those fuzzy yellow balls over the court can be tiring! Jacob Stap, a tennis camp instructor from Wisconsin, decided to invent a device to make this task easier.

Stap added a handle to the top of a wire basket. Pushing down on the ball with the basket would cause the ball to hop up into the basket and keep it from falling out of the bottom.

Stap received US Patent 3,371,950 in 1968 for his tennis ball retriever and storage unit. Then he started his own business to make and sell his invention.

The walk back to the car was sooo long.
And sooo hot. Brooke didn't think she was
going to make it. Then, she heard a familiar

doo-doo-do-do-doo-doo

from across the street...

Harry Burt invented two summer traditions: ice cream bars and ice cream trucks! Burt owned an ice cream shop and wanted to create a new treat. He coated a square of vanilla ice cream in a thin layer of chocolate. Burt's daughter tried it and said it was messy, so he added a stick.

Burt received US Patent 1,470,524 for his process of making frozen treats in 1923. Next, he had to figure out how to sell his ice cream bars. Instead of putting them in stores, Burt bought a set of trucks and hired drivers to drive around neighborhoods selling ice cream. It was a hit!

What great luck! Everyone agreed—
ice cream was the perfect treat on
this sweltering summer day.

"Brookie, let's play another game," Noah said when they got home. But what should they play?

"I want to dance!" Brooke said as she put on a sparkly pink tutu.

"Dancing is fun but I don't think it's a game," Noah said. "I want to win at something. How about basketball?

The tutu was first worn in 1832 at the Paris Opera. It was designed by French artist Eugène Lami and worn by Italian ballerina Marie Taglioni.

The skirt on the tutu was shaped like a bell and made of layers of stiff fabric. This made the tutu look full while still being light enough to dance in. Lami's tutu was also cut off above the ankles, which was very short at the time!

Brooke and Noah quickly learned one thing about basketball: the goal was really high! And worse, they had no way of lowering it.

Then an idea dawned on Brooke. If she couldn't bring the goal closer to her, maybe she could use her ballet shoes to bring herself closer to the goal.

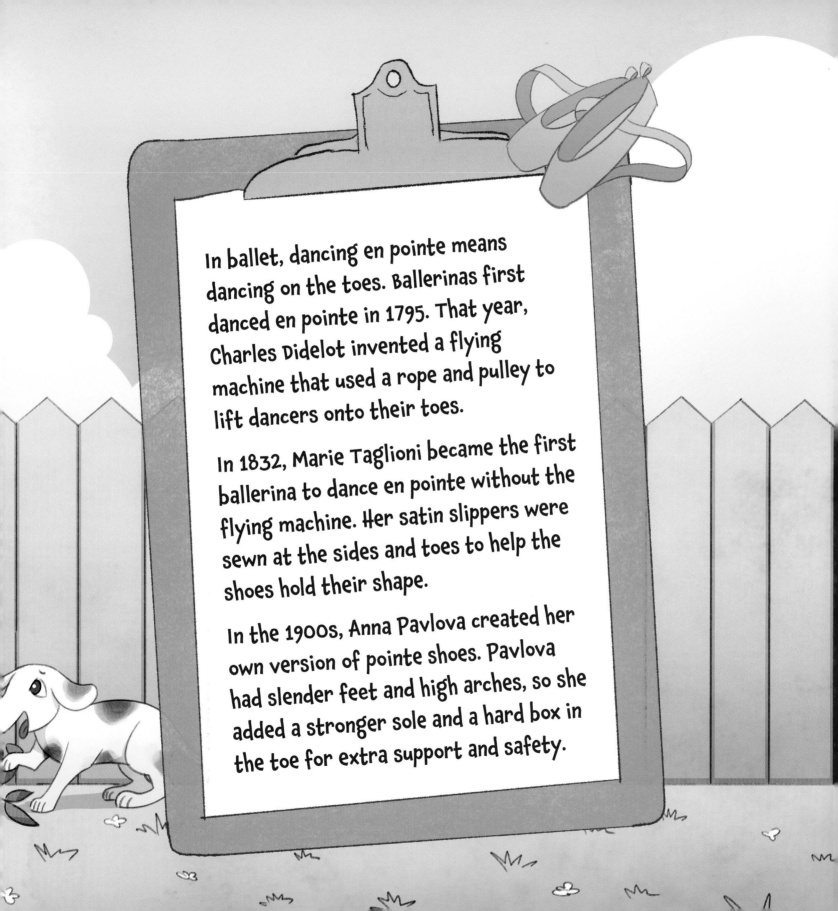

In ballet, dancing en pointe means dancing on the toes. Ballerinas first danced en pointe in 1795. That year, Charles Didelot invented a flying machine that used a rope and pulley to lift dancers onto their toes.

In 1832, Marie Taglioni became the first ballerina to dance en pointe without the flying machine. Her satin slippers were sewn at the sides and toes to help the shoes hold their shape.

In the 1900s, Anna Pavlova created her own version of pointe shoes. Pavlova had slender feet and high arches, so she added a stronger sole and a hard box in the toe for extra support and safety.

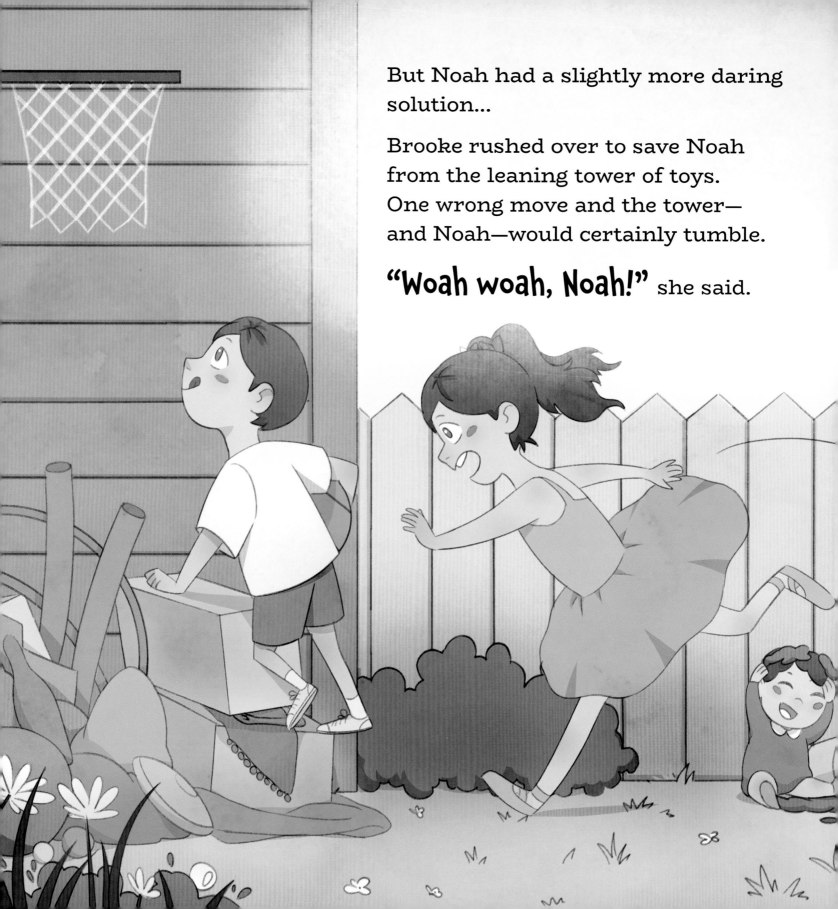

But Noah had a slightly more daring solution...

Brooke rushed over to save Noah from the leaning tower of toys. One wrong move and the tower— and Noah—would certainly tumble.

"Woah woah, Noah!" she said.

James Naismith invented basketball in 1891. Naismith was a PE teacher and wanted to create a sport that could be played inside during winter.

Naismith used rules from soccer, hockey, and football for his new game. He attached a peach basket high up on a wall, and players would shoot a ball into the basket to score points.

The first basketball games were played in 1892. Over time, peach baskets were replaced with metal rims and cotton nets and a backboard was added. Basketball is now one of the most popular sports in the world.

"Let's play soccer next," Brooke said. But her soccer ball was as flat and lumpy as an old pillow. They would have to improvise.

"What if we use these beach balls?" Noah asked. "I bet they will be extra bouncy!"

"Good idea! And maybe my ballet shoes will make them bounce extra far when I kick them."

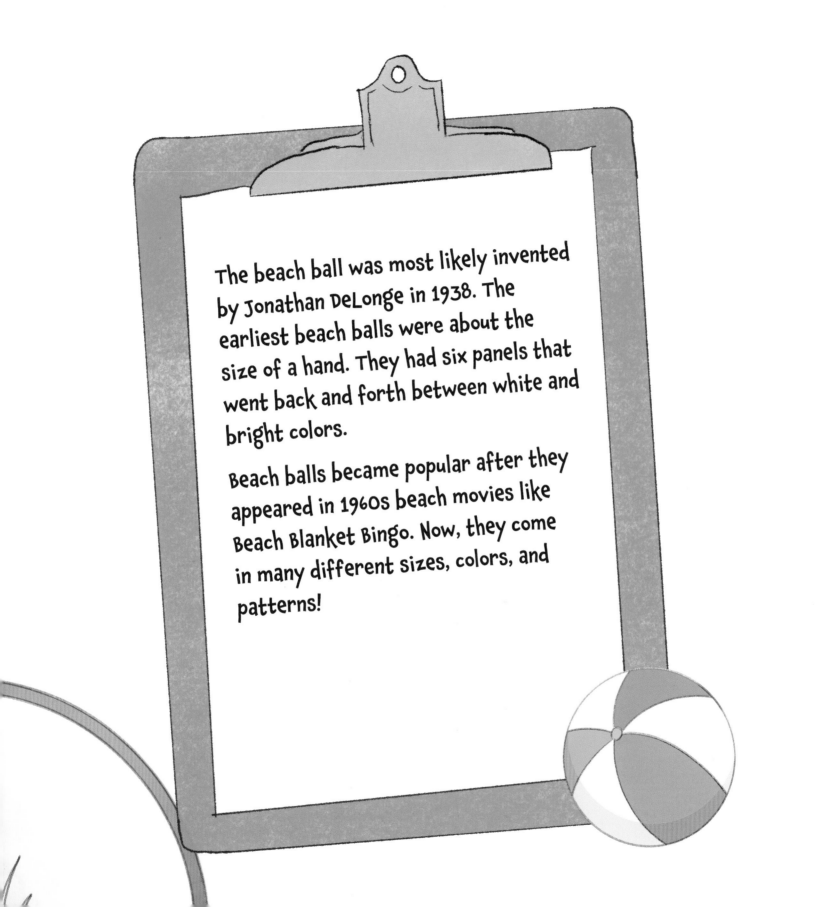

The beach ball was most likely invented by Jonathan DeLonge in 1938. The earliest beach balls were about the size of a hand. They had six panels that went back and forth between white and bright colors.

Beach balls became popular after they appeared in 1960s beach movies like Beach Blanket Bingo. Now, they come in many different sizes, colors, and patterns!

Noah dug through the pile again and finally pulled out a croquet mallet.

"I bet I can hit the beach ball farther than you can kick it!" Noah said as he whacked the ball with the mallet.

"You're on!" shouted Brooke. She pirouetted into a kick and jetéd after her beach ball.

Brooke kicked her ball across the yard, but Noah was sure he could do better. Noah walloped the ball with all his might...

...and it sailed right over the fence.

"I'll get it!" Noah said.

He was nearly at the top of the fence when Brooke spotted the big hairy spider sitting on top.

"Woah woah, Noah!" she said.

As Noah scurried down, his beach ball sailed back over the fence. He turned to Brooke with a puzzled look on his face.

Then there was a voice from the other side of the fence. "Did you lose a beach ball?"

It was Maggie! Maggie lived next door and liked to come over sometimes.

"Thanks!" Noah said. "Do you want to stay and play with us?"

"Sure! What are you playing?"

INVENTOR PROFILE: MARILYN HAMILTON

Marilyn Hamilton is an American athlete and inventor. In 1978, an accident left her unable to walk. Hamilton and two friends made a special wheelchair so she could keep living an active life.

The wheelchair was lighter and easier to move than the wheelchairs that were used back then. In 1980, they started a company to make and sell their invention. The Quickie Wheelchair Company still exists today.

Hamilton won the National Wheelchair Tennis Singles in 1982 and 1983. She also won a silver medal at the 1982 Paralympic Ski Championships. Today, Hamilton is an advocate for people with disabilities.

"We played ballet basketball and now we're playing beach ball croquet," Brooke answered. "What do you like to play?"

"I like to dance and play basketball, too. And sometimes I play golf with my dad!" Maggie said. "But maybe we can play something new today?"

Brooke felt the gears in her brain start turning. A new sport they could play? Hm...

The answer came to Brooke like switching on a light. What if they combined all three of Maggie's favorite sports into one super fun game?

And so they set off to find what
they needed for their new game...

...in every toybox...

meow...

...in every cabinet...

...and in every basket...

...until they had everything they needed for dancing bean bag golf.

Bean bag golf was simple—and fun!

And the best part was that everyone could play together.

They played three rounds and the game was tied. "This game should be harder," Noah said.

He looked around for somewhere else to throw his bean bag. "I bet I can hit that bee hive!" Noah shouted as he reared his arm back.

But Brooke and Maggie were masters at avoiding disaster.

"Woah woah, Noah!" they said.

Hula hoops have been around for thousands of years, but they first became popular in the US in the 1950s.

In 1948, Richard Knerr and Arthur Melin started a toy company. Their first hit was the frisbee, but the second wasn't far behind. In 1958, the company trademarked the name Hula Hoop. Then they began making them out of a new kind of plastic called Marlex. They sold nearly 20 million hula hoops in the first six months and 100 million in two years!

In 1963, Arthur Melin received US Patent 3,079,728 for his hoop toy.

What's a fun game you can create with things you can find at home?

That night at dinner, Brooke and Noah told the family about the games they had invented.

"Can we invite our friends over tomorrow to play with us?" Noah asked. "I want to show them our new sports."

"And everyone can wear their princess dress or superhero cape!" Brooke added. "And we can make healthy snacks to share with everyone."

"Of course we can have a party," Mom said. "No dream is ever too big. I'm sure your friends would love to play your new sports."

The next morning, everyone got to work setting up for the party. Noah's job was to make his favorite snack, ants on a log. But Noah was much better at eating ants on a log than he was at making them.

"Woah woah, Noah!" Grandpa said. Busted!

Marcellus Gilmore Edson invented peanut butter in 1884. First, Edson removed the shells from the peanuts. Then he ground up the peanuts in a mill used for grinding flour.

The mixture was soft like butter when it cooled, so Edson added sugar to make it thicker. He was granted US Patent 306,727 in 1884.

Edson wanted to use peanut butter to make candy, but Dr. John Harvey Kellogg thought it would be a healthy option for people who could not eat solid food. He invented his own process for preparing nutmeal and received US Patent 580,787 in 1897.

Brooke's job was to make Gatorade slushies. She added the ingredients to the blender, put the lid on, and pushed the red button.

SPLASH!

The lid shot off the blender like a rocket! The colorful contents of the blender splattered all over the kitchen and coated the room in a sticky blue mess.

"Woah woah, Brooke!" Mom said as she rushed to put the lid back on.

In 1965, a football coach at the University of Florida saw that his players were getting sick during games even though they were drinking lots of water. The coach was worried about the players' health, so he teamed up with scientists to find an answer.

The scientists figured out that water wasn't replacing the nutrients the players used during games. They decided to create a drink that both hydrated and replaced nutrients. They added salt and sugar to water and lemon juice to make it taste better.

The drink was named Gatorade in honor of the school's mascot, the alligator. Today, athletes all over the world drink Gatorade.

Soon the backyard was filled with princesses and superheroes. They played ballet basketball...

...and beach ball croquet...

...and bean bag golf.

And everyone had fun and
no one realized they weren't
keeping score.

A new thought came to Noah. "Brookie, I'm starting to think that winning isn't the most important part of playing sports."

"Maybe the important part is having fun with your friends," Brooke said.

"Your friends AND your big sister," Noah added.

Brooke smiled at her little brother and put an arm around his shoulder. "Noah," she said, "I think this is the start of a beautiful team."

RULES FOR DANCING BEAN BAG GOLF

Find 3 items that you can safely throw bean bags into. These items will be the goals for the game. Each item should be a different size. Then, arrange the items in a line from largest to smallest. Some examples of things you can use: hula hoops, empty boxes and bins, or laundry baskets.

A few feet away from the goals, create 3 lines on the ground at different distances. You can use chalk if you're playing outside. You can also use jump ropes, yarn, or sticks.

The youngest player goes first. Starting at the closest line to the goals, they must first do a dance move, and then they can throw 3 bean bags. The closest goal is 1 point, the next-closest is 2 points, and the farthest goal is 3 points.

The second youngest player goes next. They must do the first player's dance move and then add one of their own. Then they can throw their 3 bean bags. If a player misses a dance move, they lose 1 point. This repeats for all players until everyone has had one turn. After each player has had a turn, round 1 is over.

Everyone moves to the middle line, and the dance moves reset. The oldest player goes first this time. Round 2 ends once everyone has completed their second turn.

In round 3, the youngest player once again goes first. The game ends once every player has completed their third turn. The player with the most points at the end of round 3 wins!

Your court should look like this:

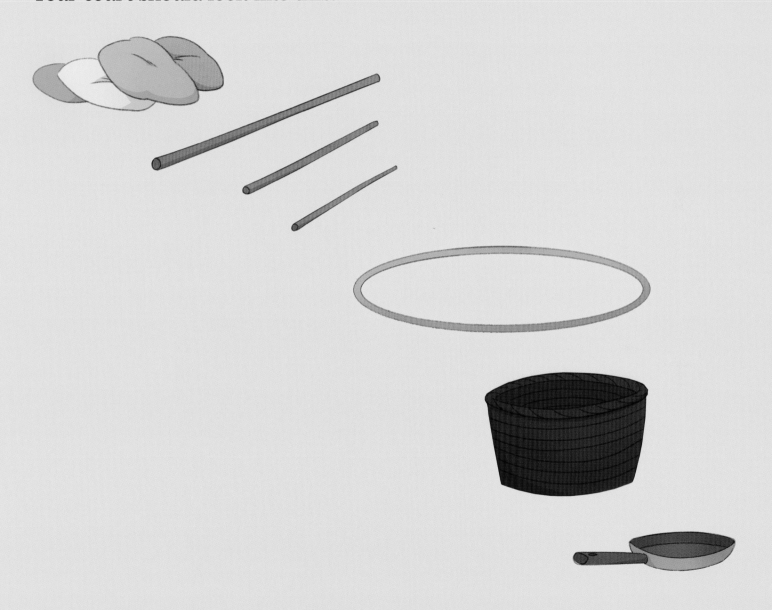

Need a way to keep score? Go to **ifnotyoubooks.com** to download and print out Brooke and Noah's special score cards!

TIMELINE OF INVENTIONS

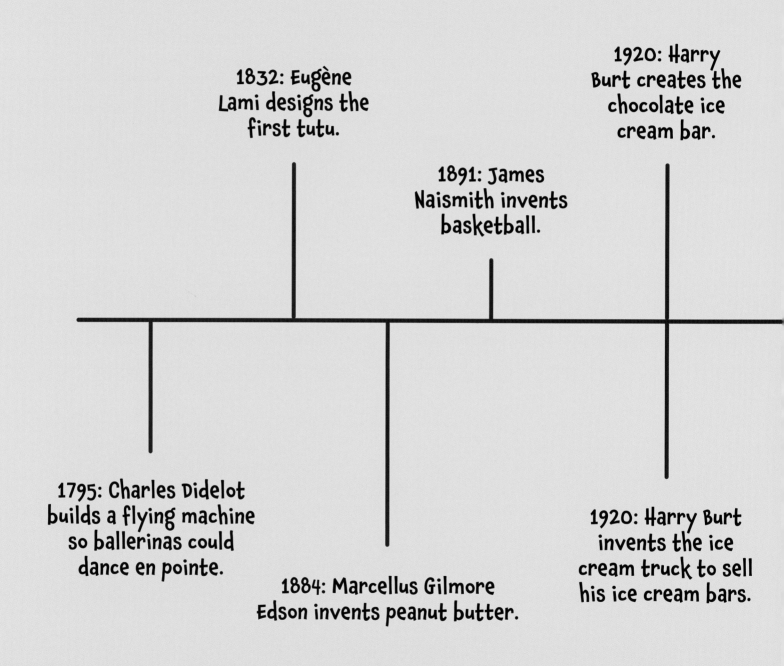

1832: Eugène Lami designs the first tutu.

1920: Harry Burt creates the chocolate ice cream bar.

1891: James Naismith invents basketball.

1795: Charles Didelot builds a flying machine so ballerinas could dance en pointe.

1884: Marcellus Gilmore Edson invents peanut butter.

1920: Harry Burt invents the ice cream truck to sell his ice cream bars.

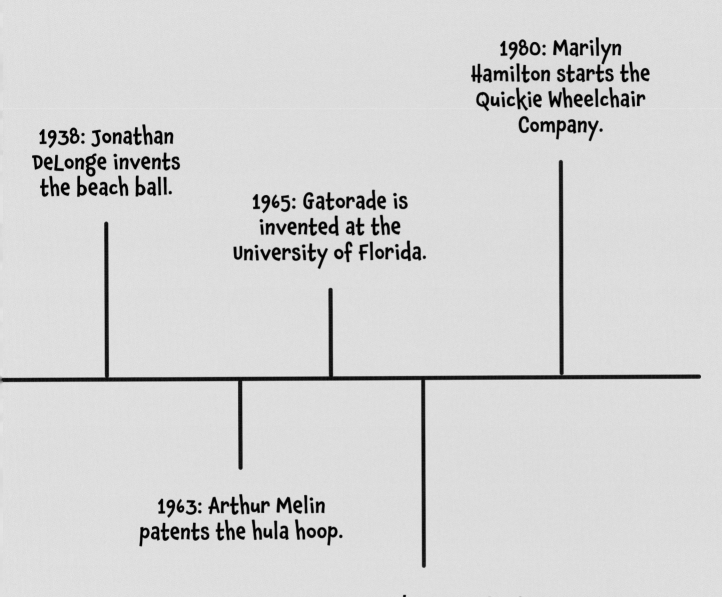

THINGS TO KNOW ABOUT PATENTS

What is a patent?

A patent is a kind of **intellectual property**. The person who holds it can prevent others from making, using, or selling their invention for a set amount of time.

Intellectual property is a "creation of the mind." Inventions, books, drawings, and brand names are all forms of intellectual property.

What can be patented?

Any device or discovery that uses a new process, machine, or material can be patented. Improvements to existing devices and discoveries can also be patented.

Are there different kinds of patents?

Yes! Utility patents protect the way a device is used, made, or operated. Design patents protect the way it looks.

How long do patents last?

Utility patents are granted for 20 years from the date the application is filed. Design patents are granted for 14 years.

Who can apply for a patent?

Anyone! According to patent law, an inventor (or someone who is helping them) map apply for a patent for their work.

IF YOU ENJOYED LET THE GAMES BEGIN, THEN YOU'LL LOVE

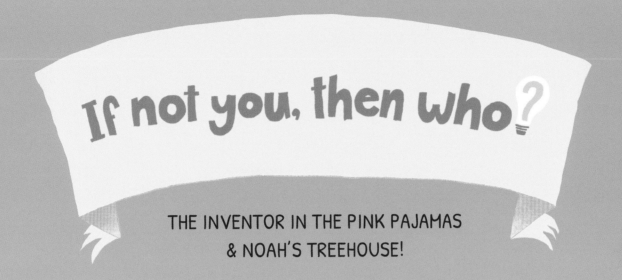

THE INVENTOR IN THE PINK PAJAMAS
& NOAH'S TREEHOUSE!

In volume one of the If Not You, Then Who? series, readers will follow Brooke through the course of an ordinary day in her life. In volume two, you'll spend the day with Noah as he builds his dream treehouse. As Brooke and Noah explore the origins of the inventions around them, they imagine new gadgets that they could invent and hopefully inspire young readers to envision their own!

We are planning a whole series of books, and we welcome your ideas! Join our mailing list at kids.weeva.com or follow us on Facebook or Instagram @IfNotYouBooks. You'll be the first to know about new releases, fun activities, and special promotions.

We can't wait to hear from you!
David & Emberli

P.S. Reviews are a helpful tool for future readers, and we'd be honored if you shared your thoughts about this book with others.

David and Emberli Pridham make their homes between Dallas, Texas and Barrington, Rhode Island along with their children Brooke, Noah, and Graham and their cat, Miss Beasley. David is the CEO of Dominion Harbor Enterprises, a patent transactional firm based in Dallas, Texas.

MADE WITH LOVE IN TEXAS

Printed in the USA